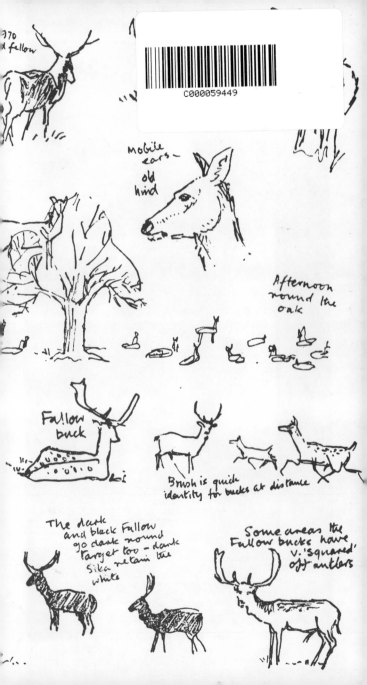

370
d fellow

Mobile
ears—
old
hind

Afternoon
round the
oak

Fallow
buck

Brush is quick
identity for bucks at distance

The dark
and black Fallow
go dark round
Target too - dark
Sika retain the
white

Some areas the
Fallow bucks have
v. 'squared'
off antlers

FIELD GUIDE TO
BRITISH DEER

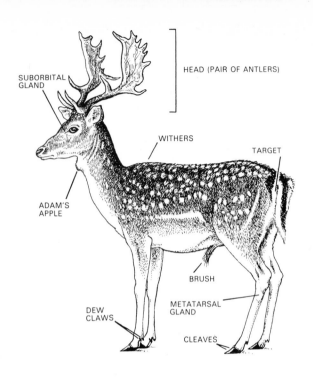

SUBORBITAL
GLAND

HEAD (PAIR OF ANTLERS)

WITHERS

TARGET

ADAM'S
APPLE

BRUSH

METATARSAL
GLAND

DEW
CLAWS

CLEAVES

Fallow buck in late September

FIELD GUIDE TO
BRITISH DEER
THIRD EDITION
COMPILED AND EDITED BY
F.J. TAYLOR PAGE

Illustrated by Michael Clark

PUBLISHED FOR THE BRITISH DEER SOCIETY
BY BLACKWELL SCIENTIFIC PUBLICATIONS
OXFORD LONDON EDINBURGH
BOSTON MELBOURNE

© 1971, 1982 by Blackwell Scientific Publications
Editorial offices:
Osney Mead, Oxford OX2 0EL
8 John Street, London, WC1N 2ES
9 Forrest Road, Edinburgh, EH1 2QH
52 Beacon Street, Boston, Massachusetts 02108, USA
99 Barry Street, Carlton, Victoria 3053, Australia

First published 1957
Second edition 1971
Third edition 1982

Taylor Page, F.J.
  Field guide to British deer.—3rd ed.
  1. Deer—Great Britain—Identification
  I. Title
  599.73'57   QL737.U55

  ISBN 0-632-00978-0

DISTRIBUTORS
USA
  Blackwell Mosby Book Distributors
  11830 Westline Industrial Drive, St Louis, Missouri 63141

Canada
  Blackwell Mosby Book Distributors
  120 Melford Drive, Scarborough, Ontario, M1B 2X4

Australia
  Blackwell Scientific Book Distributors
  214 Berkeley Street, Carlton, Victoria 3053

Photoset by Enset Ltd,
Radstock Road, Midsomer Norton, Bath, Avon
Printed in Great Britain by Butler & Tanner Ltd,
Frome and London

'Above all things let not the devil tempt you to trifle with a deer's nose. You may cross his sight, walk up to him in a grey coat, or if standing against a tree or rock near your own colour, wait till he walks up to you, but you cannot cross his nose even at an incredible distance, but he will feel the tainted air. Colours and forms may be deceptive or alike; there are grey, brown and green rocks and stocks as well as man—and all these may be equivocal—but there is one scent of Man and that he never doubts or mistakes; that is filled with danger and terror; and one whiff of its poison at a mile off—his nose to the wind—and the next moment his antlers turn and he is away to the hill or wood—and he may not be seen on the same side of the forest for a month.'

Sobieski J. and Stuart C.
Lays of the Deer Forest, 1848

Introduction

Since the *Field Guide to British Deer* made its appearance in 1957 considerable progress has been made in our understanding of the wild deer of this country. Many more people have found that deer provide abundant interest for leisure time. Naturalists, photographers, film-makers and artists have used their knowledge to open up new avenues of study. Research into the behaviour, parasitology, pathology and physiology of the deer species has made rapid development. The distribution of deer in Britain and Ireland has been much more closely watched, and during the last few years a National Survey has added considerably to our knowledge. No county is without some deer, and with the continued wider dispersal of deer of at least three species increases are to be expected. Already several Welsh counties have reported deer where hitherto it was believed none existed. The red and roe deer of Scotland are renowned, and in Ireland herds of three species are attracting renewed attention.

Our intention in 1957 was to provide a simple guide to the study of deer mainly for the beginner. The book seems to have achieved that purpose for the number of deer watchers rapidly increased. Deer are attractive creatures, and as opportunities for watching them became more frequent, especially through the much valued collaboration of the Forestry Commission, information concerning the detection of the presence of deer and the recognition of each species proved a valuable asset.

Many others whose work brought them into contact with deer—foresters, pest control officers, stalkers and gamekeepers—found in the book information unobtainable in any other publication. The proper management of deer made it important that accurate details concerning deer populations and the correct identification of each species became part of the working knowledge of those responsible.

6

After more than twenty years of critical trial by many observers and practical field naturalists, the *Guide* has stood the test of time. But it has become clear that recent knowledge must now be incorporated and the book made more efficient for use in the future.

Our hope that the interest in British deer would be stimulated, and hasten the day when they would receive fair treatment, came nearer to reality when the several Deer Acts and other relevant legislation was passed by Parliament, laying down Close Seasons and rules for the control of deer and the marketing of venison. This legislation is summarized on pp. 75–7. A comprehensive Wildlife Act was passed in Eire in 1975. We welcomed the very important change in policy of the Forestry Commission whereby deer were no longer regarded as vermin but accepted as a natural part of the forest structure. Control societies have to a large extent replaced, by selective control with the rifle, the inhumane and inefficient deer drives of the past.

Much remains to be done to safeguard our deer. They are for all to enjoy, and it is hoped that in its new form this book will attract many more to share in the pleasure that these fine animals can give.

The following pages contain all that is necessary for the identification of the five species of deer most commonly at large in Great Britain and Eire. Here they are in order of size:

Red deer	*Cervus elaphus*
Fallow deer	*Dama dama*
Japanese sika deer	*Cervus nippon nippon*
Roe deer	*Capreolus capreolus*
Reeves's muntjac (barking deer)	*Muntiacus reevesi*

Other species which may be found in limited areas of the British Isles:

Reindeer	*Rangifer tarandus*
Chinese water deer	*Hydropotes inermis*

are referred to on pp. 41 and 78, and pp. 17, 40 and 52. The first part of the book deals with identification. The second with various aspects of deer biology which give a fuller understanding of each species.

The book is in sections as follows

Acknowledgements

When the *Field Guide* was first produced it owed its inspiration to many members of the Deer Group, at that time a specialist section of the Mammal Society. Since then the activities of the Group, particularly those involving the taking of an energetic lead in working for the better treatment of deer in Britain, led to the development of an independent deer society. In 1958 the copyright of the *Field Guide* was generously presented to the British Deer Society by the Mammal Society and we take this opportunity to acknowledge this and express our gratitude to their Council.

The original contributors were

P.H. Carne   Jim Taylor Page
J.S.R. Chard   Victor Ross
Peter Delap   Henry Tegner and
Herbert Fooks   G. Kenneth Whitehead
Gerald Johnstone

The illustrations were by

Herbert Fooks
Jim Taylor Page and
Victor Ross

The *Guide* met with considerable success and became the accepted handbook not only for beginners but also for all students of deer. It achieved recognition as a valuable and informative synthesis of concise facts and helpful detail. It was acknowledged as a text book for foresters and those concerned with control, and a reference book for research workers and for amateur naturalists alike in this country and abroad.

The book has now been entirely revised and recast in a new and modern form while retaining most of its original features. The illustrations are almost entirely the work of a very accomplished artist, Michael Clark. We are much

10

indebted to him for the care he has devoted to the work and for his advice on the presentation of the text. Specialist advice has been freely given by A. Cadman, J. McCurdy (N. Ireland), M. Clark, F. Courtier, O. Dansie, P. Delap, M. Horwood, J. Hotchkis, J. King, G. Logan (Scotland), E. Masters, F. Mulloy (Eire), D. Talbot and C.G. Wright, who also supervised revision of the third edition. The Editor is indebted to all whose suggestions have been incorporated to make the new *Field Guide* more useful, and particularly to the publishers for their cooperation in bringing it to a successful completion. The original section on Tracks by J.S.R. Chard has been retained with little alteration.

The endpapers are especially to be commended and are an integral part of the book. They demonstrate the way in which a field naturalist can catch with his pencil the moods and attitudes of deer which words are inadequate to express.

How to Use the Field Guide

Unless you have beginner's luck, it is unlikely that you will find and see deer at your first attempt. It is not easy and you must follow some simple rules.

Take into account the *Habitat* of each species of deer described on pages 14–17. This will give you an idea of where and in what type of country you are likely to find the deer you are looking for. Then take a preliminary walk looking for the *Signs of the Presence of Deer* listed on pages 13–14.

The clearest indications of the presence of deer are the *Tracks* they make. These are described and illustrated on pages 17–25. Be careful not to confuse the tracks of deer with those of cattle, sheep or other livestock. With experience you should find that you can follow deer paths successfully through woodland. This will tell you much about how deer live and the places most used in their activities at the time of year of your visit.

Look out for *Droppings* like those shown on pages 28 and 29. These give you a little help in confirming species, size and sometimes sex of the deer present, but use such evidence with caution, and do not rely solely upon it.

The real excitement and interest comes when you see your first wild deer. You must follow the rules governing approach and observation (pages 31 to 34). Deer have highly developed senses of smell, hearing and sight. As you may get only glimpses of your quarry, the *Guide* stresses the importance of the sounds made by deer. See *Voice* (pages 35 to 37), which the deer may give if they see you before you see them. The *Identification* features on pages 38 to 41 will give you much assistance in the confirmation of your preliminary observations. Associate very carefully the appearance of the deer with the time of year.

Once you have learned to stalk your deer you will want to know more about them. Their *Antler Development and Age* (pages 42 to 48); their *Seasonal Change of Coat* (pages 49 to 52); their *Gait* (pages 52 to 55); all may prove additional means of identification and extension of interest.

If you intend to make a special study of deer, you will need to know their *Feeding Habits* (pages 55 to 57), and their *Herd Activities* (pages 58 to 61). Variation in habits and behaviour are shown in the *Seasonal Behaviour Charts* (pages 63 to 66). No chart is given for the muntjac, each individual having its own succession of activities regardless of season.

Be sure to keep notes and sketches of what you see, setting them down at once if possible. In the Appendix you will find a Glossary of technical and other terms used to describe deer and the forest. These are of value in reduction of description. Guidance is also given on measurement and counting, and sources of information of many kinds in places and books.

Signs of the Presence of Deer

Once a suitable location for deer has been decided upon, preliminary investigation can be very helpful in confirmation of the presence and even the species of the deer there.

1 Tracks. The most significant and useful evidence. See p. 17.

2 Droppings. Important but requiring caution. See p. 27.

3 Creeps and runways. Deer make regular use of paths, often parallel to those made by human beings and 10 yd or so in cover, leading to significant areas—feeding grounds, rutting stands, resting places. Look for entries into thick undergrowth, creeps under fences and worn trackways down banks. Narrow pathways in thick, low vegetation may indicate the presence of muntjac.

4 Fraying stocks. Mention of these is made on pp. 60 and 61. Trees freshly marked in this way are a very good indication of the recent presence of deer. Those found from April to July are almost certainly made by roe deer or muntjac.

5 Thrashed bushes and rubbed trees. See pp. 58 and 59.

6 Bark stripping. Particularly a habit of red, fallow and occasionally sika deer, in late winter and early spring.

7 Bole-scoring of large trees. Most characteristically done by sika and fallow deer, though occasionally by red deer.

8 Ground scrapes and pits. It is important to distinguish them from the dust baths of pheasants. On a larger scale are the stamping grounds of small herds of fallow, red and sika deer. Assemblies on a relatively small patch of ground produce a considerable disturbance. This is sometimes found round a tree stump or even a telegraph pole or bole of a tree.

9 Bedding places. Areas corresponding roughly with the size of the animals, and sometimes associated with marked discoloration of the grass. Fallow deer may use hollows full of dead leaves.

10 Wallows. These are peat-, water- and/or mud-filled hollows used by red and sika deer during the rut. They usually show signs of considerably activity. Wallows may also be used during spring and summer by both sexes.

11 Cast hair. Wallows often contain masses of cast hair. Look also for sign of hair from deer on barbed wire fences particularly where deer pass under fencing wire; also in bedding places.

12 Play and rutting rings. Fallow and roe deer make these. Play rings are used by fallow bucks in February and March and by does and fawns in August and September. Roe rings are made and used by does and kids during June and early July. The roe buck may chase the doe and produce much worn circular pathways round a focal point, a tree or bush for example. The early rutting rings in July are large; the rings become much decreased in size as the rut reaches its height in late July and early August.

13 Browsing. Close scrutiny of plants will show where stems have been cut within a deer's reach—the browse line.

14 Rooting. The two larger species of deer are prone to root into ant hills. Roe tend to attack and break up rotten wood. Sika and fallow root out truffles.

Habitat

The natural habitat of all deer is wooded country with thick cover. If they are unmolested they may be seen grazing or resting in more open conditions, and where mountain and moorland exist red deer and sika and even roe seek cooler conditions to avoid the attention of insects. The movement of deer within their territories and sometimes over very considerable distances mainly at night offers scope for study. Records of deer in unusual places would be valuable, as would be details of regular diurnal, nocturnal and annual movements as individuals, in families or in herds.

This section will be found useful in relation to the section on Habits and Herd Activities on pages 58–61, and the Seasonal Behaviour Charts on pages 63 to 66.

Red deer

Native to forest margins of large forests. In Britain they inhabit woodlands with thick cover, and moorlands or uncultivated country near to woodlands. Where natural forest has been removed, as in Scotland and parts of England and Ireland, they have become secondarily adapted to the exposed conditions of mountain and glen. In hot weather, when it is possible, they lie up in heather on open hillsides and mountain tops where the air is cool and attack by insects is less severe.

Winter territory is usually on lower, sheltered ground.

Fallow deer

Most frequently found in lowland woods, predominantly of older hardwood trees providing thick cover. Where deer parks have existed or still exist, feral herds are likely in surrounding areas.

May be seen feeding along margins of woods or in woodland rides, and in fields nearby at dawn and dusk. In secluded localities may feed or lie out in the open by day.

The oldest bucks are almost entirely nocturnal and are thus infrequently seen, except during the rut.

Sika deer

Appear to prefer acid heathland soil. Lie up mainly in woodland during daylight hours, especially where thick cover is provided by dense hazel thickets, bramble brakes, tall bracken, rhododendron clumps and unbrashed conifer plantations. May also be found in marshy localities such as alder carrs and estuarine reed beds.

In warm weather, when troubled by flies, sika may harbour in tall corn or other field crops, and where little persecution exists they may wander abroad by day on moor and heathland. Where mountain deer forest exists they may seek the high tops rather like red deer.

Roe deer

Usually found in young plantations before the thicket stage and in woodlands with plenty of undergrowth and close to open grassy areas, forest clearings or cultivated ground. In summer, seek cool, leafy shade in bracken or other dense vegetation. May sometimes be flushed from bedding places, and if startled seek safety in flight during which a series of sharp barks may be given. See p. 37.

Where population density is high, roe will be found in all types of woodland both large and small, and anywhere else where cover and seclusion are adequate, such as isolated thickets and shelter belts, moorland scrub and coastal undercliffs. It is not unusual for roe to be found lying out in Scottish deer forest with red deer.

Early morning and dusk provide chances of observation of these deer feeding in forest rides or in open places. After rain is a particularly good time. Where little disturbed, roe can be seen fairly frequently by day, sometimes with cattle. In winter they lie up in denser woodland, especially where there are Douglas firs or unbrashed pine trees.

Where reed beds exist alongside a forested area some roe are likely to be found. A marsh or other source of water will attract these deer, although there are some places, such as woodlands on chalk downland and scrub on limestone pavement, where many roe live remote from surface water and where the only sources of supply are dew and in the food taken.

Muntjac deer

Almost exclusively in woods with low, tangled brambles and similar undergrowth. Muntjac are easily hidden and may exist undetected in such conditions for a considerable time. Their presence may be suspected if narrow runways are found. It is less likely if there is a close canopy and little undercover. They will live temporarily in standing crops.

Most frequently seen in the evening and very early morning in open grassy places or nearby cultivated fields where feeding is likely to occur but they regularly feed in dense cover also. Acorns, chestnuts and crab apples are attractive to these small deer and they should be looked for where such supplies exist in autumn.   '

Muntjac can sometimes be flushed from dense brambles in winter time. Regularly used pathways may then more easily be found, leading to feeding places and bedding areas. Look for their tracks (p. 24) and droppings (p. 28).

Chinese water deer

Brief mention must be made here of this species, limited mainly to woodlands near parks from which they have escaped. With an increasing number of wildlife parks, and a tendency for the adoption of deer as pets, one or more may be found in unexpected places. Confined and localized mainly to parts of Bedfordshire and Shropshire.

Tracks

The first indication of the presence of deer in a new area will probably be given by their tracks. The ability to read these tracks accurately is essential for those who wish to study such elusive animals. With some initial instruction and much practice it is possible to become proficient. A tape measure or folding rule and a pair of dividers should be carried, and the tracks of all deer seen should be carefully measured and recorded.

The recognition of fresh tracks will provide information as to the places most frequented by deer and where they may be watched for. Detailed examination will reveal variations in the size, shape and arrangement of the tracks, leading eventually to an understanding of the gait and positive identification of the species. The final achievement is to be able to estimate from tracks the sex and approximate number of deer in a particular cover.

This is done by 'ringing', that is, making a circuit of the area, and is best carried out after dawn or as soon as the deer have settled for the day. New tracks show up well in dew or hoar-frost, or after a fine night following rain or snow. The freshness of a track is gauged by making a mark beside it, and comparing its appearance with that of the track. Slots show up more plainly when viewed against the low sun of morning. After a dew, grass holds down when trodden. If deer are being followed when this has occurred the tracks look light, but if the observer is moving in the opposite direction to the deer the tracks show up darker.

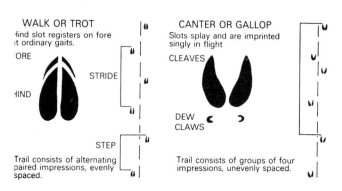

WALK OR TROT
Hind slot registers on fore it ordinary gaits.

FORE

HIND

STRIDE

STEP

Trail consists of alternating paired impressions, evenly spaced.

CANTER OR GALLOP
Slots splay and are imprinted singly in flight

CLEAVES

DEW CLAWS

Trail consists of groups of four impressions, unevenly spaced.

Fig. 1

All passes, entries, galleries and racks (see Glossary, p. 68) are checked, and foiled tracks (tracks in grass) followed up until slots are found. Individual tracks are memorized and the number entering an area balanced against those leaving it. Large areas are ringed in sections by following rides and streams, but always working up wind so that deer are not moved on to ground which has yet to be searched.

The tracks of deer differ from those of cloven-hoofed domestic animals (cattle, sheep, goats and pigs) as follows:

1 The slots are narrow in proportion, the cleaves taper to a point and the heels are rounded, never sharply defined.

2 The tread is mainly on the toes, and the cleaves normally close along their whole length, splaying only in soft ground or in flight.

3 The hind feet register consistently and more or less completely at ordinary gaits.

4 The prints lie more or less closely along one median line.

5 The step is relatively long in proportion to the size of foot.

The form of the slot and the pattern of the trail are modified not only by gait, but also by size, age, type of ground, condition and sex. In doubtful instances the effect of these must be understood and taken into account before a definite identification of the species can be made. In the larger species of deer, individual variation is usually sufficiently marked to enable the tracks of one animal to be followed among others of the same kind, and to be recognized again later on. Final judgment must never be given on a few slots, but only after the trail has been followed sufficiently to show which features are consistent and reliable.

Slot and gait

In all species except muntjac there is no general difference (except perhaps an individual one) between the slots of opposite sides. There is often some difference in shape between the fore and hind slot, however, and in all species the hind slot is rather shorter than the fore. As the hind slots come uppermost when the prints register, they serve as the main basis of comparison. Their shape, size, depth and position are all significant. Variations in gait do not assist much with identification, and the principal comparisons must always be related to the normal walking pace. This is recognized by a regular step and consistent registration, with all the prints falling neatly into line. In these conditions, the length of step is constant for each individual; this and the width of the slot across the heel are the key measurements.

Terrain
The influence of ground conditions on the form and pattern of the tracks becomes evident to a practised observer. The effects are discounted by following each trail as far as possible across different types of ground until a fair sample of tracks has been examined and their normal appearance can be deduced. The softer the ground, the larger is the print.

Size and age
In a young deer, the slots are small, shallow and short; tread is on the toes, and the cleaves are sharp pointed and

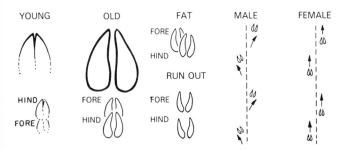

Fig. 2

normally shut. In an old deer, the slots are large, deep and long; tread is more on the heels and the cleaves are worn and blunt. They tend to splay, and the fore cleaves are often kept open.

The step of a young deer is short, and that of an old deer is long. This difference increases with the pace, and when moving together, the younger is usually the first to change gait. At a normal walk, the average stride is roughly equal to the height at the shoulder; a young deer tends to over-reach slightly but consistently with the hind feet and an old deer consistently steps short.

Condition

This varies according to season. In a fat beast or a female heavy in young, the hind slots are placed somewhat to the side of the fore, the prints are deeper, and the sway is increased. The fatter the deer, the greater is the sway. With animals in poor condition, such as males exhausted after the rut, the hind slots drop behind those of the fore, and may fail to register altogether.

Sex

Differences in the tracks are slight when young, but become more definite with age. In two animals of differing age showing the same length of step, the younger animal is the male, e.g. the step of a four-year red stag is about the same as that of an old hind. As a rule the slots and step of a mature male are quite one-fifth greater than those of a mature female of the same species. His far heavier weight helps to develop other characteristics. Thus his slots are longer and deeper, and in proportion relatively broader. His fore slots are relatively longer in proportion to his hind, and the fore cleaves show a tendency to splay. The shape of the cleaves is more obtuse, and their edges less sharp. In species which use them, the dew claws are larger in proportion, more prominent and less sharp; they splay more widely, pointing outwards rather than downwards.

His step is not only longer but more regular, the sway is normally greater, and he tends to point his toes outwards. In the female, registration is frequently more accurate but generally less consistent, her step is uneven and the toes normally point directly forward.

IDENTIFICATION

Figure 3 on page 24 shows the tracks of the hind foot of mature male deer of each species, for comparison of size and shape. The average length of step is given in the accompanying description given below. These also refer to mature males in each instance.

The tracks of females and young have the characteristic shape somewhat modified by the factors given on the preceding page, but they are still recognizable if these factors are correctly taken into account. Allowance must be made for a proportionate reduction in the size of slot and the length of step.

Red deer

Slot large, *c*. 2½ in (6 cm) wide at heel. Step 2 ft (60 cm) or more at a normal walk. Fore and hind slot not dissimilar. Cleaves short in proportion, somewhat rounded. Marks of dew claws prominent in flight.

Fallow deer

Slot medium, *c*. 2 in (5 cm) wide at heel. Step 1¾ ft (52·5 cm) at a normal walk. Fore and hind slot not dissimilar. Cleaves long in proportion, somewhat straight-sided, with little tendency to splay. Marks of dew claws rare.

Sika deer

Slot medium, slightly under 2 in (5 cm) at heel. Step about 1½ ft (45 cm) at normal walk. Fore cleaves elongated, tending to splay. Hind cleaves short and rounded, normally shut at heel. Marks of dew claws frequent.

Roe deer

Slot medium, *c.* 1½ in (3·6 cm) at heel. Step about 1¼ ft (37·5 cm) at a normal walk. Fore and hind slot not dissimilar. Cleaves narrow in proportion, evenly tapered, somewhat open at the heel with much tendency to splay. Marks of dew claws prominent in flight.

Muntjac deer

Slot small, *c.* ¾ in (1·5–2 cm) at heel. Step about 8¼ in (21 cm). Cleaves may register unevenly with medial cleave slighter but often symmetrical. Dew claws may register occasionally in deep mud.

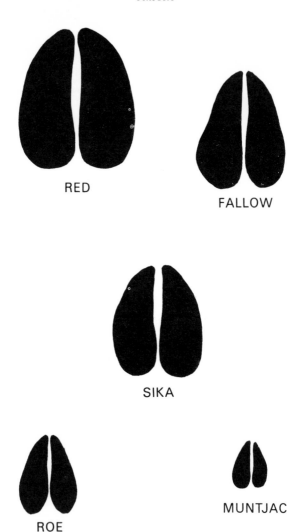

Fig. 3. Mature adult male hind foot tracks, half natural size

COMPARISON WITH DOMESTIC ANIMALS

In all species the points vary widely according to breed as well as age and sex. The following diagrams are therefore given only as examples and will not be typical in every locality. The prints of some breeds are more deer-like in appearance, and others less so.

The prints in Fig. 4 are of adult males—hind foot—in each instance, as these are more common and most deer-like.

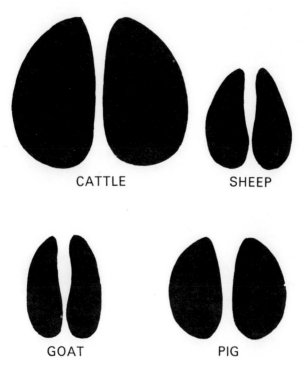

Fig. 4. Adult male hind foot tracks, half natural size

How to Make a Plaster Cast
of the Track of a Deer

Carefully remove twigs, leaves or mud that have fallen into the print. Forceps or photographers' blower brush are useful at this stage.

Mix plaster of Paris with clean water in plastic bowl

Press card (or tin) strip round track and avoid air bubbles by pouring plaster carefully onto side of track.

Check by gentle finger pressure to see if dry. This usually takes 15-30 minutes depending on how much water was mixed with plaster.

Cut out soil round plaster and remove complete. Pull back card and pack carefully inside newspaper.

Very gently wash off mud under tap. When dry, colour track or back-ground and add details.

Fig. 5

Droppings

By following a trail made by deer, you may eventually come upon their droppings (fewmets), sometimes in considerable quantities at points usually near the resting area (lair or ligging). Though by no means as certain a feature as the tracks as a means of identification, they can be used with a little experience to assist in the determination of the species and sometimes the sex, size and condition of the deer in your area. They may also be of considerable help in showing how recently the area has been used by deer.

This evidence must be used carefully, because of possible confusion with the droppings of other animals but also because shape and size are very variable even within the same species. Only average specimens are shown below, natural size.

Red deer (Fig. 6)

Occasionally adherent. Light-brown to black acorn-like form, slightly concave at blunt end. The pointed opposite end fits into the concavity of the previous dropping.
In June heaps of fewmets (crotties) are frequently adherent.
In July the individual fewmets are longer and harder.

Before the rut, when the stag is fat, droppings resemble small 'cow-pats'. During the rut they become small and misshapen, when the stag is taking very little food.

Fallow deer (Fig. 7)

When fresh look glossy. Sometimes adherent and faceted. Generally smaller than red deer. Usually black. Often in heaps but in string if animal is moving.

Sika deer (Fig. 8)

Not noticeably adherent. Frequently found in heaps. Not

Stag   Hind

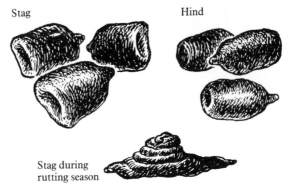

Stag during
rutting season

Fig. 6. Red deer (natural size)

Buck

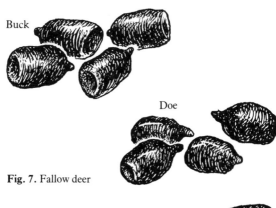

Doe

Fig. 7. Fallow deer

Fig. 8. Sika deer   **Fig. 9.** Roe deer

Fig. 10. Muntjac deer

Goat:
non-fibrous
externally;
non-adherent

Sheep: faceted;
usually adherent

Rabbit:
fibrous;
non-adherent

Hare: very fibrous;
non-adherent

Fig. 11. Other species for comparison

easily distinguishable from roe, though shiny green if fresh
and dull green or black if old. Male dropping larger than in
roe. Sexes similar.

Roe deer (Fig. 9)

Non-adherent or exceptionally so. Usually single. Dark
brown or black and somewhat glossy. Often accumulated
near bedding area. Similar appearance in both sexes.
Slightly thinner than in sika.

Muntjac deer (Fig. 10)

Faceted, with small terminal point. Usually spread as
individual pellets often in considerable numbers in one
place. Many adhere as crotties. Typically black and shiny.
Same appearance in both sexes.

Always allow for size, particularly from May to December
while the fawns are growing up.

Introduction to Deer Watching—
High Seats

THREE STEEL MANUFACTURED HIGH SEATS

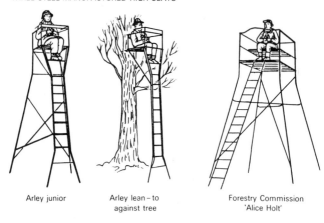

Arley junior

Arley lean-to
against tree

Forestry Commission
'Alice Holt'

HIGH SEATS MADE IN WOOD

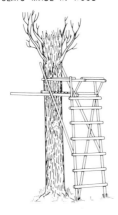

Rope on
both sides

Lean-to high seat
(courtesy of the
Forestry Commission)

Ladder seat supported by
two struts with rope round
tree.

Fig. 12

Introduction to Deer Watching

The hints on stalking and watching given in this section have been culled from the experience of many who have been or still are old hands at the game. The beginner will find them worthy of careful attention.

CLOTHING

This should be comfortable and adapted to season and weather. Colours should blend with the surroundings and materials must allow easy, silent movement. Rustling mackintoshes are most unsuitable. Use a wind-cheater, sports jacket or similar lightweight coat. The most suitable colours are olive-green, khaki or a green and brown mixture. The important thing is to try and merge oneself with the background. A deerstalker hat is most useful headgear, providing shade for the eyes and some camouflage of the face. For footwear on easy ground rubber-soled shoes are comfortable and noiseless. Wet feet do not matter so long as you keep moving. If the ground is rough wear shoes or sandals with thick rubber soles, and for mountainous country rubber-soled boots, should be chosen.

EQUIPMENT

Field glasses are essential. Clear vision in fading light is more important than magnification and it is advisable to have all optical surfaces bloomed. Magnifications of 8×30 or 7×50 are suitable, combining reasonable magnification and field with a weight which will not become burdensome. The deer photographer will require a telephoto lens with a wide aperture. A small tripod is almost essential. Cine-cameras also require a tele-lens. The filming of deer requires special techniques to overcome the noise of the camera.

A haversack or rucksack is useful for small equipment but some find that they can carry what they need in large pockets. An insect repellant is important. A tape measure or a walking stick marked in feet and inches will find frequent use. Avoid anything that rustles, rattles or shines.

STALKING TACTICS

Tactics vary according to the type of country. When the probable location of the deer is known, a careful and quiet approach must be made, using whatever cover is available and having regard to wind direction. Alternatively, one can build a hide in a likely place and avoid a stalk, waiting for the deer to come out at dawn or dusk. Sometimes it is necessary just to hunt in likely areas, moving very slowly and sitting, kneeling or standing motionless very frequently. A deer watcher should train himself to stand absolutely still. The flicker of an eyelid can easily cause a deer to move off at a critical moment. Practice makes it possible to detect a motionless deer, however well camouflaged it may be against its surroundings. Learn to watch instinctively for horizontal intrusions into a vertical tree trunk pattern. The aim is to outwit the excellent sense of smell and hearing and the power of noticing movement which deer possess.

Always stalk against the wind and check its direction frequently. Move slowly, stand often, look around and listen. Never cross open spaces without stopping in cover first to spy the area. Especially after rain, deer frequently can be seen standing in the open drying themselves. Take great care to avoid any noise—loud talking, or coughing, or any metallic sound such as the knocking of field glasses against camera. The cracking of a stick is not serious if you stand still afterwards for a minute or so and do not make the same sound repeatedly. Deer make quite a lot of noise themselves when confident that there is no one about. Move so that you keep in perfect balance, otherwise you will not be able to 'freeze' suddenly when necessary. Get to know your ground thoroughly by walking about in it under many different conditions, and if possible alone. Only in this way will you have sufficient experience to vary your approach in changing conditions of wind and light.

The best times for a stalk are usually the very early morning just before dawn, and in the evening about sunset and on into the dusk. But there are places where deer may be found all the day long, especially during the rut. It is most important not to follow them into their sanctuaries in order to get a closer view. They always choose dense cover and they will most certainly detect your presence. Any disturbance may cause them to leave the area altogether.

When you get deer in sight, stand still unless you are in good cover yourself. Do not move until you are sure that all the deer have their heads down. Generally you should not try to get nearer than approximately fifty to eighty yards. You should also get away from the deer after your watch without disturbing them, moving as unobtrusively as you came. The less they know you are about, the better your chance for future observations. If deer are on the move and you keep perfectly still with the wind in your face, they may pass within a few yards of you.

Deer watchers should not enter privately owned land without obtaining prior permission from the owner. Apart from common courtesy, game shooting or deer culling may be seriously interrupted by unexpected trespassers.

DEER WATCHING FROM HIDES AND HIGH SEATS

For much closer views the use of a high seat is to be recommended. Various types, from simple ladders to portable tubular steel frameworks to those seating several people, are shown on p. 30. The siting of these requires not only knowledge of the forest but also the habits of the deer in the particular district chosen. You must know their regular tracks and feeding places, their assembly points and rutting grounds. The position will depend upon these and the conditions of prevailing winds. Never site the hide on or very close to a deer path; put it at least four yards to one side of the path. A carefully prepared stalking path must be made to the hide and always used with caution.

There are three ways of 'waiting': in the ground, on the ground, and above the ground. The first two require only a simple hide. The above-ground watching point has several advantages. Most important of all is that the watcher is independent of the wind and his movement is less restricted. The modern hut on stilts also provides shelter from weather, though its use requires considerable care in the avoidance of extraneous noise.

Whatever method is chosen, it is essential to take up your position well before the approach of the deer. It follows that the waiting method is better suited for the afternoon and evening and the stalk for the early morning, unless one is prepared to spend a night out.

Voice

Deer are normally silent animals. Badly scared deer tend to depart unobtrusively, but an observer approaching deer closely may himself be startled by the warning call of the species. Although failing to see the animal, he may be able to identify it by the sound it makes.

Very characteristic calls are also made by the males of the species during the rutting period. Most females and young keep in contact by bleating and piping cries.

Red deer

This species is characteristically silent.

The stag gives a rare warning bark if in danger. It also grunts when worried by flies.

The hind likewise makes little sound except for a gruff bark as a warning to her calf on her return to it. She can and does give a more frequent nasal bleating call, and a crisp warning bark if suddenly disturbed.

The calf has a high-pitched bleat. If alarmed it gives a scream. At rutting time the stag 'roars', especially at first and last light. The sound resembles the bellow of a bull but with deeper intonation, and usually ends in several grunts. Woodland stags often give a single resonant groan at long intervals.

Fallow deer

Also generally silent at the adult stage.

The doe gives a whining bleat as a call to the fawns.

The fawns communicate with the does by plaintive nasal bleating which increases when they are pestered by the bucks. It sounds like 'mee-ulk'. A doe with a fawn will also give a crisp and resonant bark as a warning call when disturbed, and the buck may give a similar bark, more especially at rutting time.

The typical voice of a fallow buck in rut is a rather fast and continuous belching snort with a marked rhythmic intonation. In still weather it is audible well over half a mile away.

Sika deer

Generally silent unless alarmed.

The call of stag and hind when alarmed is a short, sharp, screaming whistle ending in a grunt, often repeated several times with a time lag of 15–20 seconds between each call.

The hind uses a similar call when guiding a calf through undergrowth. It is used most frequently in summer and can be heard up to a distance of half a mile, being more drawn out if the animal if merely suspicious. Peevish squealing of the stags occurs, especially in high winds, and continues into mid-winter.

The rutting call is impossible to confuse with that of any other deer at large in Britain and Eire. The stag makes a whistle, rising to a crescendo and declining down scale to a concluding grunt, usually uttered three or four times in rapid succession. The stag is then silent as a rule for at least ten to fifteen minutes, and often for as long as half an hour. It is heard chiefly at dusk or in the early morning and might be compared to the noise of a gate swinging on rusty hinges. A rutting sika is difficult to locate by its call owing to these long periods of silence. It is much easier to locate red deer and fallow deer by their rutting calls.

Another type of rutting call usually made by stags accompanied by hinds is a single drawn out querulous whistle rising to a peak, tailing off and ending in a grunt uttered every two or three minutes. A stag challenges with a sound rather like the expulsion of air through closed lips. A low bleat or grunt is uttered in the vicinity of a hind in season.

When on heat, sika hinds have a special bleat, rather plaintive and subdued. This sound is irresistible to an unmated stag.

The calf bleats like a fallow fawn. The sound can be imitated by blowing on a blade of grass held between the thumbs.

Roe deer

Both buck and doe can give a staccato bark, often uttered as the animal takes flight. The bark of the buck is gruff, shorter and less continuous than that of the doe, which is a rather high-pitched and terrier-like sound. The barking may continue for some time as the animal moves off into the distance.

The deeper the call, the older is the deer.

The doe calls to the kids with a high-pitched 'pee-you' or 'peep-peep'. She also makes a faint and high-pitched piping note which the buck can hear at a considerable distance, and to which it responds immediately by coming in seach of the doe. This sound, which is made at the rutting time, can be imitated by the use of a specially made roe-call.

The kids give a shrill, lamb-like bleat.

At the rut, the buck grunts when pursuing the doe or a rival.

Muntjac deer

Both sexes can give a single, loud bark, repeated at intervals of four to five seconds for a period of up to an hour. They do this when disturbed, separated or excited, or when the does are in oestrus.

Does and fawns will squeak if disturbed by other animals. A separated fawn has a characteristic pathetic bleat, uttered with the same frequency as the adult bark but in a very much higher pitch.

Muntjac also grunt and produce clicking sounds. They have a most piercing and distressing cry when in extreme difficulty.

Identification *(next to 6 ft man)*

RED STAG   AUGUST TO FEBRUARY

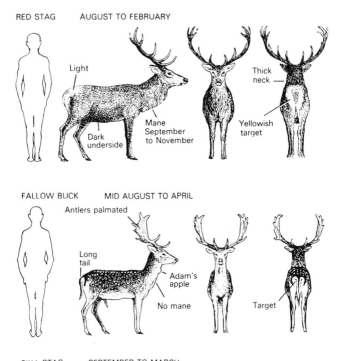

Light

Dark underside

Mane September to November

Thick neck

Yellowish target

FALLOW BUCK   MID AUGUST TO APRIL

Antlers palmated

Long tail

Adam's apple

No mane

Target

SIKA STAG   SEPTEMBER TO MARCH

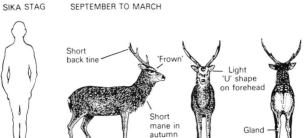

Short back tine

'Frown'

Light 'U' shape on forehead

Short mane in autumn

Gland

Fig. 13

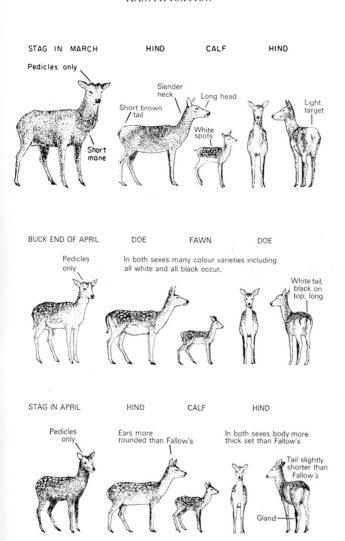

STAG IN MARCH   HIND   CALF   HIND

Pedicles only

Slender neck

Long head

Short brown tail

White spots

Light target

Short mane

BUCK END OF APRIL   DOE   FAWN   DOE

Pedicles only

In both sexes many colour varieties including all white and all black occur.

White tail, black on top; long

STAG IN APRIL   HIND   CALF   HIND

Pedicles only

Ears more rounded than Fallow's

In both sexes body more thick set than Fallow's

Tail slightly shorter than Fallow's

Gland

39

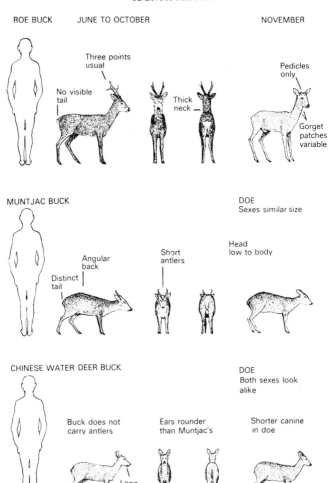

ROE BUCK JUNE TO OCTOBER NOVEMBER

Three points usual

No visible tail

Thick neck

Pedicles only

Gorget patches variable

MUNTJAC BUCK DOE
Sexes similar size

Angular back

Distinct tail

Short antlers

Head low to body

CHINESE WATER DEER BUCK DOE
Both sexes look alike

Buck does not carry antlers

Ears rounder than Muntjac's

Shorter canine in doe

Long canine

Fig. 14

ROE DOE IN JUNE
Sexes similar size

KID

Spotted

DOE IN DECEMBER

Slender neck

Distinct white tuft

MUNTJAC DOE

Short tail, white underneath

FOX

Long tail white tip

HARE

CHINESE WATER DEER

'Button' – like eyes and nose

REINDEER BULL

Herd near Aviemore, Inverness

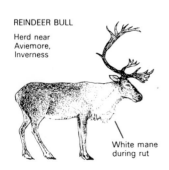

White mane during rut

COW

Bulls and Cows bear antlers, but Cow's smaller. Bulls shed December, Cows after calving in spring

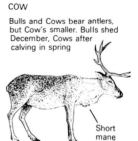

Short mane

Antler Development and Age

Statements concerning the age and growth of antlers must always be made with the greatest caution. Size and the number of tines or points are, for example, a very inadequate indication of age. Although antlers are shed and re-grown annually as a general rule, exceptions do occur. Their development depends upon such widely differing factors as heredity, health, food and weather. To be dogmatic would be misleading. The diagrams on the pages that follow (pp. 43 to 48) show normal heads of the five species. Variation can be very extensive and it would be true to say that it is very rare indeed for two heads to be exactly alike.

As a rule, as deer age they are inclined to follow the same kind of development as a human being—youth and sprightliness, middle age and 'spread', older age with well-developed, rounded hindquarters. Gradually as the curves disappear and the joints stiffen, senility becomes apparent.

A stag in its fifth year should have 'all his rights', that is, brow, bay and tray tines on both antlers (see p. 68). Many, however, miss a bay. The characteristics of the antler form are inheritable and a male deer will transmit to its offspring the power to produce a good or bad head. Management of wild and park deer is concerned in part with the production of deer with fine heads. Selective culling is concerned with the removal of poor stock and older beasts to maintain the correct numbers.

The focal point in the yearly life of a deer is the rut. The production of antlers plays an important part in this. They develop very rapidly. In a red deer it takes only about three and a half months. The enormous drain on the animal's strength during this relatively short period of growth is much influenced by the climate and the availability of food.

HOW ANTLERS GROW

January 7/8 months

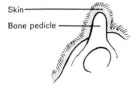

Skin
Bone pedicle

May/June
12/13 months

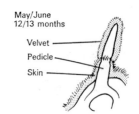

Velvet
Pedicle
Skin

July/August 14/15 months

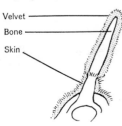

Velvet
Bone
Skin

End September
16 months

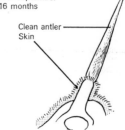

Clean antler
Skin

Stag will carry his first head
until the following March/April

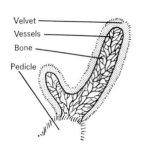

Velvet
Vessels
Bone
Pedicle

A growing antler is really the
continuation of the pedicles
and is fed by veins which lie
under a soft covering skin
— velvet. When antler is
fully formed these recede
and skin dies and is rubbed
off leaving uncovered bone—
antler

Fig. 15

43

Antlers are bony outgrowths from the skull. Over the surface of the bone and within it lie the blood vessels which help to supply the growing structure with food and the calcium salts for its growth. Covering each antler is a soft, furry skin called velvet. When growth has reached its maximum for the year, the blood vessels shrink in size, the velvet shrivels and dies and it is then frayed off. The antlers are now fixed to the head by what are in effect immovable ball and socket joints. The new growth of antlers starts almost immediately as the old antlers loosen in these sockets and eventually fall off. In most species this occurs well after the rutting season. If the antlers were to be cast at the end of the rut, it would probably be beyond the energy of most beasts to survive the double burden of growing them and keeping themselves alive during the bleak winter months.

As antlers are not a criterion of age, other sources of age determination have been sought. The degree of wear of the teeth is one possible, though by no means absolutely certain, indication. It is always wise in preparing a skull for mounting to retain the lower jaw for tooth examination.

ANTLER DEVELOPMENT AND AGE— RED DEER

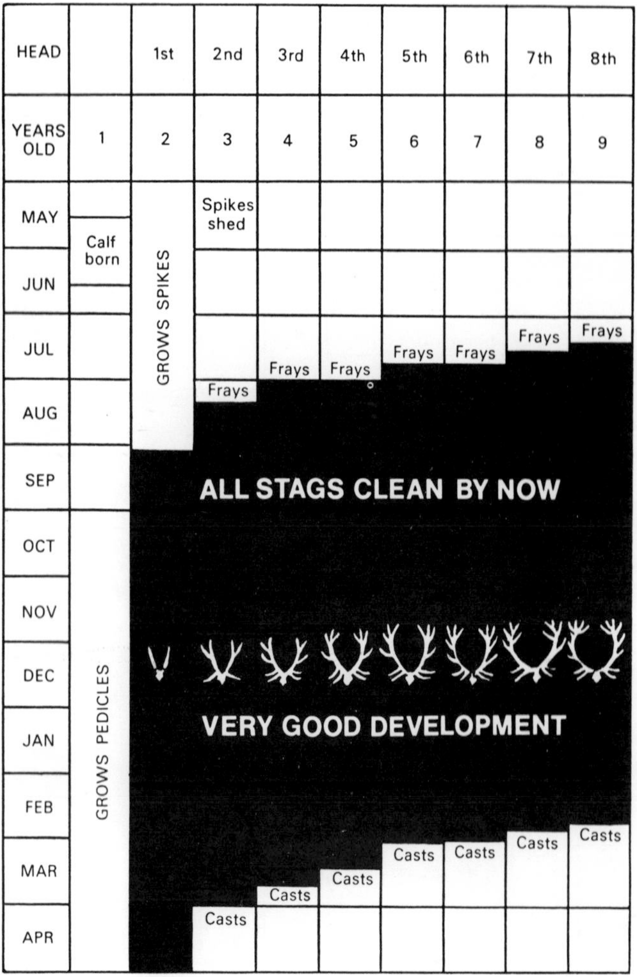

HEAD		1st	2nd	3rd	4th	5th	6th	7th	8th
YEARS OLD	1	2	3	4	5	6	7	8	9
MAY			Spikes shed						
JUN	Calf born								
JUL		GROWS SPIKES				Frays	Frays	Frays	Frays
AUG			Frays	Frays	Frays				
SEP									
OCT									
NOV									
DEC	GROWS PEDICLES								
JAN									
FEB									
MAR					Casts	Casts	Casts	Casts	Casts
APR			Casts	Casts					

ALL STAGS CLEAN BY NOW

VERY GOOD DEVELOPMENT

Fig. 16

ANTLER DEVELOPMENT AND AGE— FALLOW DEER

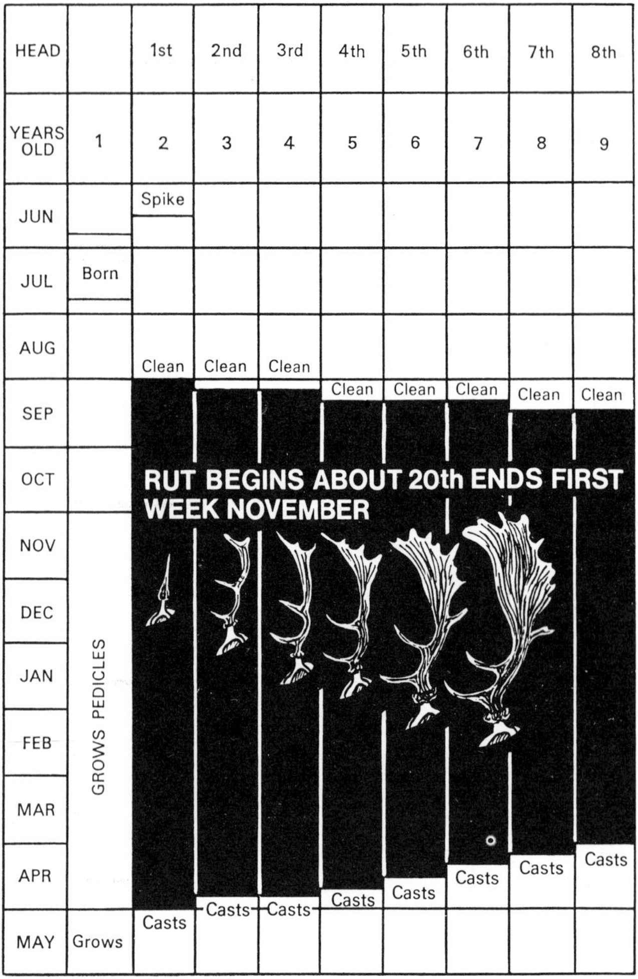

HEAD		1st	2nd	3rd	4th	5th	6th	7th	8th
YEARS OLD	1	2	3	4	5	6	7	8	9
JUN		Spike							
JUL	Born								
AUG		Clean	Clean	Clean					
SEP					Clean	Clean	Clean	Clean	Clean
OCT		RUT BEGINS ABOUT 20th ENDS FIRST WEEK NOVEMBER							
NOV									
DEC	GROWS PEDICLES								
JAN									
FEB									
MAR									
APR					Casts	Casts	Casts	Casts	Casts
MAY	Grows	Casts	Casts	Casts					

Fig. 17

46

ANTLER DEVELOPMENT AND AGE— SIKA AND ROE DEER

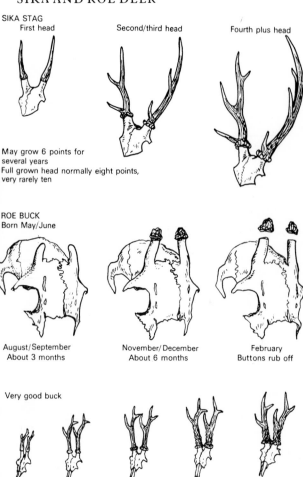

SIKA STAG

First head   Second/third head   Fourth plus head

May grow 6 points for
several years
Full grown head normally eight points,
very rarely ten

ROE BUCK
Born May/June

August/September   November/December   February
About 3 months   About 6 months   Buttons rub off

Very good buck

First   Second   Third   Fourth   Fifth

Fig. 18. Antler development and age—sika and roe deer

ANTLER DEVELOPMENT AND AGE— MUNTJAC DEER

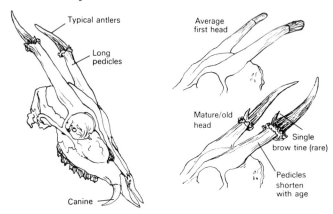

Typical antlers

Long pedicles

Canine

Average first head

Mature/old head

Single brow tine (rare)

Pedicles shorten with age

Fig. 19. Antler development—muntjac buck

HEADS OF THE SMALLER DEER FOR COMPARISON

Fig. 20. Left: Muntjac buck in velvet of second head
Centre: Chinese water deer buck
Right: Roe buck in velvet
Inset: Roe buck with perruque head due to injury to testicles.

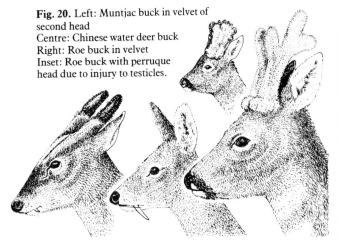

48

Seasonal Change of Coat

Deer shed their heavier winter coat in spring, and as winter again approaches they develop a thicker one. This seasonal change often involves a change of colour. Although it is impossible to mention every modification likely to be found, the most important ones for each species are given. Notable differences are well worth recording.

Fawns are generally spotted, a protective camouflage in shade under bracken or heather with sunlight filtering through.

Red deer

Summer: Considerable variation is found. Grey, dark reddish-brown, deep brown or buff coats may be seen. The inner sides of the thighs are creamy yellow and the rump light grey. A line of dark hair is sometimes found down the back. The tail is tufted and about 6 in long. A well-developed mane is produced before the rutting period in September. Older stags retain this mane throughout the year. Younger ones lose much of it when the winter coat is shed in May.

Winter: Coat rough and thick; dark brown, greyish brown, or grey colour, often looks dirty, especially after wallowing (see p. 58). Change of coat commences in May; at this time tufts of shed hair found in the wallows.

Calf: Dark brown on back and flanks, and spotted with white. Spots lost within six weeks as uniform dull brown, fluffy coat is grown.

Fallow deer

There are at least four colour varieties and many intermediate forms exist due to interbreeding.

Common: Various shades of chestnut with prominent

cream or white spots on flanks in summer. In winter they become darker. The spots are lost. Rump white, edged with black. Black line down back on to tail.

Menil: As above but spots retained in winter. Rather brighter coloured than common. Rump and underside of tail white, not edged with black.

Black: Dark chocolate to almost intense black, without white rump. Spots only visible at close quarters. Greyer colour in winter.

White: Really cream-coloured. Fairly frequent where inbreeding common, as in parks. True albinos are rare.

In all the change to a thicker coat occurs during October and the summer pelage is regained in the following May.

Fawns: Common and menil have large white spots. Black fawns have spots visible only in certain lights. White fawns show only a difference in tone where spots should be.

Sika deer

Summer: Flanks a warm buff brown, spotted with yellowish white though much less conspicuously than in common variety of fallow. Usually a row of white spots on each side of dark dorsal stripe. Stags are darker than hinds. The dark stripe usually continued down dorsal surface of white tail. Characteristic white hairs over metatarsal gland on hind legs.

Winter: Longer and darker coat, sooty brown above and greyish brown below, without spots. Stags look almost black from a distance. Hinds conspicuously grey. Head paler and grey at all times. Black-edged white rump patch very conspicuous in both winter and summer. Expands noticeably when deer is startled or takes flight. Fallow deer tail much longer and much blacker on the dorsal side. Characteristic U-shaped eyebrow stripe, lighter in colour than rest of head.

Calf: Born in summer coat, brighter than that of adult with more spots and pale brown caudal disc.

Roe deer

Summer: Bright reddish brown on back; flanks and belly paler. Dark muzzle with grey patches on each side. Ears large and black bordered. Horizontal, oval almost buff rump with no black markings. No visible tail.

Casting of coat begins in April and continues into May or even later.

Winter: Coat starts to grow in October and continues late into November. The pelage becomes greyish-brown or even grey and is composed of long, brittle, wavy hairs. Face and sides of head darker. One or two lighter patches (gorget patches) may occur under chin. Caudal disc now visibly very white. Erectile in times of stress. A white anal tuft (tush) may show clearly in adult doe. Doe also distinguishable by shape of caudal disc which is heart shaped in contrast to kidney shape in male. Where deer of pure continental origin have been introduced, winter coat is dark, warm brown. White and melanistic varieties occur very rarely.

Kid: Light brown much flecked with white. Becomes dull uniform brown within six weeks. Adult winter coat develops during autumn of first year.

Muntjac deer

Summer: Glossy bay in male with orange tinge on face and chest. Greyer and browner in female. Tail ginger above and white below. Legs dark in summer and winter. Summer pelage fully developed by May.

Winter: Longer and thicker grey-brown coat fully grown by November. No undercoat. Tail remains the same as in summer. Antler pedicles have dark brown stripe on the medial side. Does have a dark brown crown patch.

Fawns: Dark brown with light-coloured spots and clear strip of chestnut-coloured hair down back. Adult pelage assumed after about eight weeks.

Chinese water deer

For purpose of comparison, details of this deer are given.
Note that it is about the size of a muntjac and considerably
smaller than a roe doe. Coat a uniform bright chestnut
stippled with black. Head and ears buff. White around
nose, eyes, chin and inside ears. Small tail and no visible
rump patch.

Winter coat similar but duller yellowish grey. Rump
slightly paler.

Gait and Age

An observer soon discovers that each species of deer has
its typical movements and that there are recognizable
features of the gait which are related to the age of the
animal along with features of its normal development.
Some of these characteristics are shown in diagrammatic
form below.

Red deer

Red deer have a most characteristic trot. Generally the
head is held erect and steady. The movement has a
beautiful and dignified rhythm. In forest conditions the
head is thrown back with the antlers along each side of the
body.

The even-striding trot can break into canter or gallop or
reduce to a steady walk. With a single jump a 6 ft fence is
easily cleared.

Fig. 21. Red stag

Fallow deer

Move with less rapid trot than red deer. When first alarmed they are nervy and indecisive. Small parties will depart for cover at a steady, easy gallop in single file. When really alarmed they bounce away on all four legs like toys, stop at a safe distance and then continue at a rapid canter.

Fig. 22. Fallow buck

Sika deer

When first alarmed a sika tends to stand and face the source of alarm, occasionally stamping with a forefoot and craning its neck. May then advance raising each leg hesitantly—foot pointing downwards. If alarm increases, turns rapidly, jumping with all four feet together as though on springs. After a short distance is covered usually stops, advances with stilted gait and retreats again.

Advance and retreat may continue for some long time, unless seriously disturbed, when it will gallop away like other deer. An old stag tends to remain silent and motionless.

Roe deer

Move with great delicacy and care, silently pushing their way through undergrowth, nose to the ground, at a slow walk. This can, if necessary, break quickly into trot or canter. Sudden disturbance may produce a very characteristic bounding gallop bringing the head well above the herbage and allowing a view of what is ahead. This is often accompanied by barking.

Fig. 23. Roe buck

On reaching safety a roe will frequently stop and look back. When really alarmed, and when the need arises, a roe can creep almost flat along the ground. This creeping ability is used to get under wire or through a small space. A 6 ft jump is readily negotiated.

Muntjac deer

The gait can be a pottering walk with head held low, a swinging trot or a sprint at great speed. Traverse dense undergrowth with ease and can clear an obstacle 5 ft high.

When disturbed, runs with the tail erect displaying the white underside.

Fig. 24. Muntjac buck

Food and Feeding

It is well worth learning the signs of feeding activity left by deer. They are important in confirming the species. Deer are herbivorous ruminants and chew the cud. All deer will chew cast antlers.

Red deer

In woodlands, feed on almost any herbs, grasses and mosses. Acorns, beech mast, sweet chestnuts, hawthorn and rowan berries are taken in autumn. Bramble, ivy and yew form part of the winter diet. They are clumsy, noisy browsers, tearing down twigs of trees at 6 ft level and breaking off branches by using their antlers. No other British deer do this. They also damage pole-size trees by bark stripping at a height of about 4½ to 5 ft. In very cold weather they will feed in open fields among crops—particularly spring wheat and root crops—and where their territory abuts on to farm land damage may occur throughout the year. On open moorland and deer forest whortleberry, heather and coarse grasses are the staple diet. Near the sea, seaweed is taken during visits to the shore.

Fallow deer

Food is similar to that of red deer, but fallow roam much more in search of it and feed as they move. They are specially fond of crab apples, chestnuts and berries of all kinds. Young shoots of holly and bramble and tree branches, especially of ash and thorn, attract them. They are likewise given to marauding in crops and in gardens. In woodlands stripping of bark is confined as a rule to smooth-barked hardwoods at a height of about 4 ft. Scrapes are made in search of truffles.

Sika deer

Feeding habits appear to vary in different areas although the reason is not clear. Grass and rough herbage in the stomach indicate a predominantly grazing habit. Browsing sika frequently show by their stomach content that the staple diet is conifer needles. In some areas they prefer leaves of broad-leaved species. Sika are fond of hazel shoots, and examination of these trees is worthwhile in areas where sika are suspected. Apart from very occasional stripping of branches of medium-sized trees, they do little feeding damage to forest trees, but they will sometimes raid food crops. In coastal areas shoots of sea couch grass are much sought.

Roe deer

Roe take a very wide variety of leaves and berries as food and there are few plants in the herbage of the habitat of roe which are not used at one time or another as food. They are very fond of blackberry, wild rose and juniper, but they do not confine themselves to one food plant for very long and move from one to another steadily while browsing. They appear to seek out the succulent parts with great care, even utilizing rhododendron and privet occasionally. Fungi, pine shoots, heather and the young fronds of ferns are but a few of the items in a very varied diet. Bracken seems to be taken rarely if ever. Bark is also rarely stripped, though instances of it have been reported in severe weather.

Roe can unfortunately do severe damage in gardens.

Muntjac deer

The staple diet is bramble, ivy, grass and tree shoots. Wild fruits are taken in season. There is no significant agricultural or forestry damage but muntjac will take a wide variety of garden plants if given opportunity.

Ageing in Roe Buck

Fig. 25
Left: Young roe buck.
  Slender neck. Alert.
  Juvenile behaviour.
Left lower; Middle age.
  Plumper. Nervous.
  Throws up head frequently.
Below: Old age. Thick-set body.
  Firm rump.
  When moving smells ground.
  More shy.

Habits and Herd Activities

Knowledge of the behaviour of the individual species of deer is of utmost importance in identification, but it is important to know when to look for these characteristic activities. Reference is made here to some seasonal activities also and the time of occurrence of these is shown in the charts (pp. 63 to 66).

Red deer

Red deer are gregarious, but constitution of the herd changes with time of year. The oldest stags live apart from the herd. At the rut, stags fight to obtain possession of hinds. Just before this period they may travel very long distances. Wallows in peat or muddy pools are used by both sexes at any time of year, but most frequently in autumn. Much cast hair can be found in them in April.

Approach to any new object is made from downwind. This should be noted when placing a hide for photography or deer watching. If alarmed the hind runs with the calf. If danger continues, she will press the calf into thick undergrowth, where it lies absolutely still.

Feeding takes place usually in early morning and at night. The day is spent lying up on hill tops or in thick undergrowth. In the evening, watch can be kept for movement to feeding grounds and water in glens and river valleys. In Scotland where there is little disturbance, they are not nocturnal.

Fallow deer

These deer are gregarious but less so than red deer. When wild it is unusual for the herds to be very large (see p. 64). Wallowing is infrequent and is done by the buck only during the rut. At this season the bucks challenge and fight. Assembly points may be found—worn areas with many tracks encircling a fraying stock or rubbing tree, or stamping ground around some object. Scrapes are made like those of roe deer, but they are larger and deeper and often show marks of the antler brow tine.

Daily activity resembles that of red deer. Much of it is spent in relative inactivity lying up in deep cover of bracken, thorn scrub and so on, but if undisturbed they will often lie out in the sunlight, moving off rapidly in single file if danger threatens. At dusk they move to woodland rides and fields.

Thrashing of young trees and bushes occurs at the rut. Scoring of bark and fraying provide additional means by which the buck marks out a territory and sets his scent. Play rings may be used by young bucks in February and March, and by does and fawns in August and September.

Sika deer

Not exceptionally gregarious, even where numerous. Herds of 20–30 uncommon except in late winter and early spring. Smaller groups much more usual. Mixed herds of stags and hinds fairly common in winter, otherwise separate in quite small parties. Stags very secretive and rarely seen. At the rut, stags fight for possession of hinds. Wallows are made. Daily activity is superficially similar to that of red deer, with which they are occasionally seen when the range of the two species overlap. Fraying similar to fallow deer. Much thrashing on heather and gorse, leaving characteristic devastation on the boundaries of their territory. Within it the master stag thrashes out a rutting stand in roughly the same place each year. Bole scoring may become habitual and leads to serious damage.

When moving out to feed, small groups converge into larger parties of about twelve. Within an hour or so of dawn, they return to the thickest available cover in woodland or lie up in fields of standing crops. They are most likely to be seen in very early morning or late evening feeding in open woodland, heathland, moorland or farmland. In midwinter they become almost completely nocturnal, but they will move out and graze at intervals during the day throughout the year where unmolested.

In autumn, winter and spring, hinds and calves may associate in small troops of twos and threes up to a dozen. At 8–9 months stag calves join stag parties. Hind calves remain with hinds until about one year old. After rut, stags feed for a short time with hinds, but gradually form separate parties towards end of year.

Roe deer

Non-gregarious as a rule. Small parties may build up during the winter (see p. 66).

Roe are inquisitive and will not always move when first disturbed. They may even lie at a safe distance from forestry activities or traffic, apparently undisturbed.

At the rut, the buck pursues the does, sometimes slowly but with increasing avidity. The chase often canalizes into running in a circle round a focal point. Prior to this, from April onwards, territory is marked out by tree fraying at its borders and leaving scent from glands between the antlers and below the eyes on stems and leaves. Play areas—often with circles and figure-of-8 tracks—are used by the does and kids in June and early July. Fraying of young trees at a height of about 2 ft also occurs when velvet is being removed in early spring. As a rule the thicker the tree and the longer the fray, the older and possibly better the buck. Pawing the ground with the cleaves of the hooves leaves characteristic scrapes which identify this deer. Thrashing of tall plants such as willow herb also occurs.

In defence of its territory a buck pursues all other roebuck intruders, and short and sometimes lethal battles occur. Mating occurs between late July and early August, the doe being on heat for only a short period. Mention must be made here of the fact that, although fertilized, the egg remains only slightly developed until December, when growth becomes rapid. This unusual phenomenon is called delayed implantation. Twin fawns are not un-common, quite frequently one of each sex.

Muntjac deer

Often thought to be solitary, but probably prefer living in small family units of up to four: male, female, juvenile and fawn. Considerable aggressiveness occurs between parents and juvenile.

Continuous breeding occurs, with mating a short time after birth of the fawn. Fawns are born at approximately 7-month intervals at any time of year. Muntjac tend to live and feed in deep cover and their behaviour is difficult to watch. Bucks fray the bark of small shoots with upward movements of the lower incisors. The suborbital glands transfer scent to the white surface. Where population is high, frequent narrow or oblong shallow scrapes are made.

Although widely dispersed in cornfields in summer, there is no evidence that muntjac travel long distances at this time. The general tendency is to live and feed in deep cover and to move about only as darkness approaches.

Seasonal Behaviour

The following diagrams (Figs 26–29) represent as nearly as possible the different phases in the yearly activity of each species. Variations will inevitably be found. The period of maximum activity is represented by a vertical column running parallel with the central calendar, and between those months or portions of months concerned.

Where an activity gradually builds up or declines, this is shown by a dotted line between the earliest and latest known date. The activity of each sex is shown. Where parallel activity occurs a dotted line across the chart links the vertical indicators.

In this country, the seasons influence the muntjac in that they affect the change of pelage and movement through the countryside. There is continuous breeding with a gestation period of 210 days. Antlers are shed annually but this activity as well as pregnancy is related to each individual animal and not to the season. No seasonal chart is therefore possible for the muntjac.

RED DEER

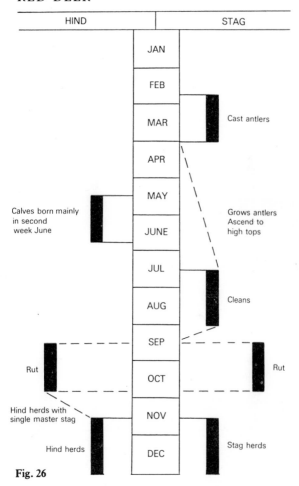

Fig. 26

[Often in summer and regularly in winter, mixed herds of stags and hinds with calves and young deer can be seen together in the Highlands. Only in late spring and early summer are stags and hinds separate.]

FALLOW DEER

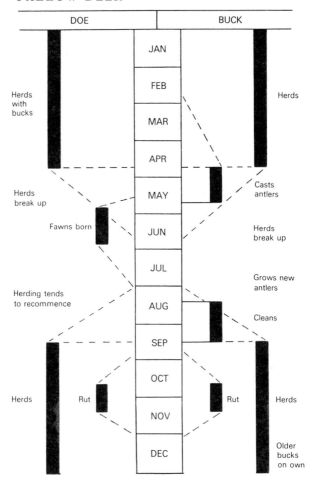

Change of pelage: see page 50

Fig. 27

SIKA

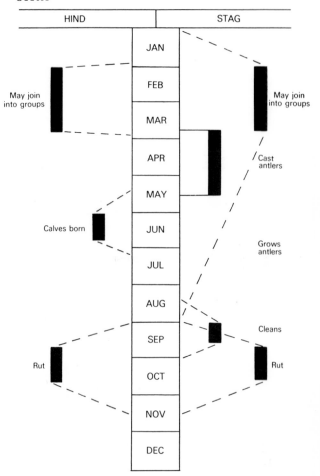

HIND	STAG

JAN

FEB

MAR

APR

MAY

JUN

JUL

AUG

SEP

OCT

NOV

DEC

May join into groups

Calves born

Rut

May join into groups

Cast antlers

Grows antlers

Cleans

Rut

Change of pelage: see page 50

Fig. 28

ROE

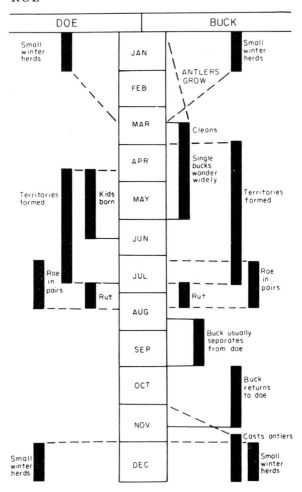

Change of pelage: see page 51

Fig. 29

Glossary

Many of the ancient hunting terms (Terms of Venery) applied to the study of deer, and many terms used in forestry, are unfamiliar to the layman. Most of the important ones are given here in classified form, in the hope that they will be adopted into the vocabulary of the deer watcher. Use of them saves much uncertainty and a great deal of time in making descriptive records. Do not be discouraged by this profusion of technicalities; it is far simpler nowadays than it used to be.

IDENTIFICATION

Albino Deer which inherits absence of pigment in hair and skin, which are white, and eyes, which are pink. Complete albinism is rare.

Antler Note differences between antlers and horns. Horns are bony outgrowths from the skull which are covered with thick and hardened skin (horn). They are never shed. Antlers are borne by male deer only, except in reindeer. They are normally shed annually and regrown at remarkable speed, usually to a larger size. They are covered with a thin, sensitive skin called velvet which dies when the antlers are fully grown and is frayed off by the deer by rubbing on bushes or trees (see Fraying).

Buck Male of the species in fallow, roe and muntjac deer. Bare buck is a 5-year-old fallow. Great buck is a fallow deer over 6 years old. In the New Forest, buck is reserved strictly for a 5 year old. See also Pricket, Sore and Sorel.

Calf The young of red and sika deer in their first year.

Crotties Heaps of droppings of deer (see Fewmets).

Doe Female of the species in fallow, roe and muntjac deer.

Fawn Strictly applied only to the young of fallow and muntjac in their first year, but a general term for all young deer in their first year.

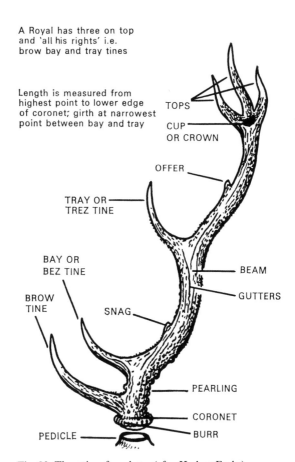

A Royal has three on top
and 'all his rights' i.e.
brow bay and tray tines

Length is measured from
highest point to lower edge
of coronet; girth at narrowest
point between bay and tray

TOPS

CUP
OR CROWN

OFFER

TRAY OR
TREZ TINE

BAY OR
BEZ TINE

BEAM

GUTTERS

BROW
TINE

SNAG

PEARLING

CORONET

PEDICLE

BURR

Fig. 30. The attire of a red stag (after Herbert Fooks)

Fewmets Individual droppings of deer.

Gorget White throat patch in roe.

Hart A rather outmoded alternative for the term Stag.

Havier A castrated deer. Castration, originally carried out in parks to improve the venison, is now rare except where the hunting of carted deer is still carried on.

Head General term to describe head and antlers of deer.

Hind Female of the red and sika deer.

Horns Alternative for Antlers in Scotland.

Hummel Male deer which fails to produce antlers, owing to a physiological defect. (Known as a Nott in the South-West.)

Kid The young of a roe deer in its first year.

Knobber Male red deer in its second year.

Melanistic Descriptive of uncommon inherited factor for a very dark pelage, mainly on back, neck and face.

Menil Variety of fallow deer in which coat remains spotted in winter.

Murderer A deer without tines on its antlers. Such antlers are murderous weapons against other deer.

Palm Palmated portion of antler of fallow buck.

Pelage The coat of a deer.

Perruque Malformation of antlers caused by accidental castration soon after antler casting. This induces formation of heavy masses of spongy tissue covered by velvet and replacing normal antlers. Normally retained for life and not cast.

Pricket Male fallow deer in its second year.

Royal A stag with 12 points (six on each antler) and with the top three on each side forming a cup or crown—hence royal. With additional points the animal is referred to as a '13 pointer', '14 pointer', etc. The word 'imperial' for a '14 pointer' is outmoded.

Single The tail of a deer.

Sore 3-year-old fallow buck.

Sorel 2-year-old fallow buck.

Spellers The top points along the palm of a fallow deer's antler.

Stag The male of the species in red and sika deer.

Switch Adult stag with no points above the brow tine. A clean switch has not even brow tines.

Target The white or paler-coloured rear end of a deer beneath the tail. Sometimes termed the speculum or caudal disc.

Velvet Furry skin covering the antlers as they grow.

Voice A red stag 'roars' or 'bells'.
       A fallow buck 'groans'.
       A sika stag 'whistles'.
       A roebuck 'bells' or 'barks'.
       A muntjac buck 'barks'.

Waster An ailing deer suffering from injury or disease.

Yeld A calfless red hind.

HABITS

Browsing Damage caused by deer when eating buds and young shoots of trees. The term applied to this mode of feeding.

Burnishing A New Forest term indicating the process of cleaning the antlers of velvet. Very often continued after velvet has been removed.

Cleaning A general term for the fraying off of velvet from the antlers on trees, bushes, heather, etc. (see Fraying Stock).

Entry Gap made by deer in a thicket or through a fence.

Fraying Damage caused to a tree when a deer is cleaning its antlers (see pp. 59–61).

Fraying stock Bush, tree or other objects used by deer during removal of velvet.

Gallery Path worn by deer in close cover; especially applied to a series of parallel routes (see also Rack).

Harbour The place where a stag lies in thick cover.

Lair or ligging The actual place where a deer lies down. A red deer 'harbours' and is 'unharboured'; a fallow deer 'lodges' and is 'roused'; a roe deer 'beds' and is 'dislodged'.

Parcel A group of hinds.

Pass The point at which deer cross a river or similar obstacle, and where they may be waited for.

Pollarding A New Forest term for the casting of antlers.

Rack The path worn by deer and marked by broken twigs.

Ring The circular path worn by deer round some focal point such as a bush (see p. 60).

Rubbing Damage caused to a tree when a deer is casting its coat.

Rut The period to, and including, the mating activities of deer, during which characteristic behaviour occurs annually.

Rutting stand The area within the territory of a stag or buck where rutting behaviour occurs.

Sanctuary That part of deer territory containing the lair.

Scrape. A patch of ground scraped with the feet by deer as part of territorial demarcation activity, often associated with fraying stocks.

Stripping Damage caused by deer gnawing the bark of trees.

Territory That area over which a male deer has active domination and which is defended against penetration by rival deer.

Wallow Where a deer rolls ('soils') in a muddy pool or peat hag (see p. 58).

TRACKS

Cleaves Two halves of the hoof or slot representing the principal toes.

Creep Worn place under wire or other fence where deer have passed.

Dew claws Vestiges of two additional toes set above and behind the cleaves. Sometimes called sur-cleaves or ergots in the stag.

Foil The tracks of a deer on grass (see also Slot).

Gait The manner of movement.

Heel trail A trail followed in the opposite direction to that in which it was made.

Misprint To step irregularly; failure to register.

Pace The speed of movement as measured by the length of step or stride.

Pattern The arrangement of footprints in the trail; variation dependent upon gait.

Register To place the hind foot in the slot made by the fore.

Signs The tokens by which to judge the species, size, age and sex of a deer. They are: the step, the entry, the fewmets and the fraying stock.

Slot The foot and hoofprints of deer in soft ground. Sometimes called 'view' in fallow and 'foil' in roe.

Splay The spread of the cleaves, particularly associated with soft ground.

Step The interval between one hoofprint and the next.

Stride The interval between successive impressions of the same foot.

Sway The deviation of prints from the median line. Most noticeable in female deer in calf (see p. 21).

Trail The sequence of footprints and other signs marking the passage of a deer. Sometimes called the Trace.

FORESTRY

Beat An area of forest under the jurisdiction of a forester.

Beating-up Replacement of the failures and losses in a plantation.

Brashing Removal of the lower branches of a plantation at the end of the thicket stage.

Canopy Continuous cover formed by the crowns of forest trees.

Compartment Sub-division of a forest used for management purposes and usually 25–30 acres.

Coppice A crop springing from the root stocks of the previous one. (Confined to hardwoods.)

Covert Small woodland or thicket serving as a refuge for deer.

Establishment The stage at which plantation requires no further attention to become an acceptable tree crop.

Final crop The best trees of a plantation, selected to grow on to maturity.

High forest A plantation continued in growth to mature stage after thinning.

Natural regeneration The self-seeding of forest trees, in contrast to sowing or planting.

Pole crop A plantation in early stages of thinning.

Rack A path cut through a young plantation to facilitate access.

Ride A wide track or break separating a forest into blocks.

Thicket The stage of growth between the closing of the canopy and the first thinning.

Underplanting The introduction of a new crop under the partial canopy of an older one.

DEER STALKING

Catch-up A procedure required when deer are to be removed from one location to another, or when handling deer is essential. A licence for this is required by law in England and Wales.

Close Season A period of the year during which the taking or killing of deer of different species is prohibited by law (see p. 75).

Conservation The action necessary to protect deer and their habitat from exploitation and the pressures upon them.

Cull A planned reduction in a herd of deer. A shooting plan designed to maintain a balance of the sexes and/or number in relation to the availability of food and living space, and to minimize damage.

Deer forest As distinct from a forest of trees, the ancient Highland forests of Scotland, long cleared of trees and now the haunt of herds of deer, retain their former name of 'forest'. A few places in England and Ireland have the same designation.

Going back The antlers of a deer past maturity progressively diminish in size and are said to be 'going back'. Disease can produce a similar effect.

Gralloch The removal of the internal organs of a deer after shooting.

Grass A stalking term frequently used to refer to the killing of a deer.

High seat An elevated structure used for watching and shooting deer (see p. 30).

Management The term used to denote the careful planning of the conservation and control of a deer population wherever necessary (see Cull).

Moving of Deer A procedure involving the movement of deer gently and without panic in a desired direction.

Paint A New Forest term for a blood-trail left by a deer which has been shot.

Selective shooting The shooting of any deer which is old, diseased or injured, or whose removal would be advantageous to the deer population in any area (see Cull).

Stalk The quiet unobserved approach to a deer for observation or shooting.

Venison The prepared flesh of a deer.

Winter feeding In any place where bad winter conditions prevail or where overcrowding might cause death from starvation, provision of food in winter may be an essential part of management.

Statutory Close Seasons for Deer
(all dates inclusive)

Species	Sex	England & Wales	Scotland
Red	Stags	1 May–31 July	21 Oct–30 June
	Hinds	1 March–31 Oct	16 Feb–20 Oct
Fallow	Bucks	1 May–31 July	1 May–31 July
	Does	1 March–31 Oct	16 Feb–20 Oct
Sika	Stags	1 May–31 July	1 May–31 July
	Hinds	1 March–31 Oct	16 Feb–20 Oct
Roe	Bucks	1 Nov–31 March	21 Oct–30 April
	Does	1 March–31 Oct	1 March–20 Oct

In addition the British Deer Society recommends the following Close Seasons for which there is no statutory provision at present:

Muntjac	Bucks	1 March–31 Oct
	Does	1 March–31 Oct
Chinese water deer	Bucks	1 March–31 Oct
	Does	1 March–31 Oct

Legislation Relating to Deer

ENGLAND AND WALES

Deer Act 1963 (Ch.36)
Roe Deer (Close Season) Act 1977 (Ch.4)
Deer Act 1980 (Ch.49)
Wildlife and Countryside Act 1981
Summary of the Deer Acts applicable to England and Wales as at January 1981. (This summary is provided for information only and constitutes no authoritative interpretation of the Acts. All who own land holding deer

or who stalk deer should familiarize themselves with the Acts.)

1 Close Seasons are specified in the Deer Act 1963 and Roe Deer (Close Seasons) Act 1977 (see table on p. 75) The Secretary of State may amend the Schedules by order.

2 Night shooting of deer is prohibited.

3 The following are prohibited as means of taking deer: traps, snares, poisons, stupefying baits, arrows, etc., and nets. Also prohibited are firearms and ammunition mentioned in Schedule 2 (1963 Act, as amended) i.e.–

Any smooth-bore gun of less than 12-bore gauge; any cartridge for a smooth-bore gun other than one purporting to be loaded with shot none of which is less than 0.203 inches in diameter (AAA) or containing a single non-spherical projectile weighing not less than 350 grams. Any rifle of calibre less than 0.240 inches (6 mm) having a muzzle energy of less than 1700 ft/lbs (235 m/kgs). Any bullet for use in a rifle not designed to expand on impact. Any air-gun, air-rifle or air-pistol.

4 Shooting from vehicles or aircraft is prohibited.

5 Driving deer by vehicles or aircraft is prohibited.

6 A constable may stop, search and arrest without warrant on suspicion; search or examine vehicles, weapons and animals; seize and detain any evidence; enter upon any land.

7 On conviction Courts may impose a fine up to £500 and/or a prison sentence of up to three months in respect of each deer taken contrary to the Acts.

Courts may also confiscate vehicles, animals and weapons (or other things) used to commit the offence. Courts may also disqualify offenders from holding a licence to deal in game and/or cancel any firearms or shotgun certificates.

There are certain exemptions under the 1963 Act from some of the prohibitions referred to above.

Venison may only be sold to Licenced Game Dealers who must maintain detailed records of all purchases.

SCOTLAND

Deer (Scotland) Act 1959 (Ch.40)
S.I. 1966 No.56 (S.4) The Deer (Close Seasons) (Scotland) Order 1966 Deer (Amendment) (Scotland) Act 1967 (Ch.37)
Sale of Venison (Scotland) Act 1968 (Ch.38)
S.I. 1969 No.794 (S.6) The Sale of Venison (Forms etc.) (Scotland) Regulations 1969

Deer legislation in Scotland differs from that applying in England and Wales in very many respects and those concerned with deer in Scotland must, necessarily, familiarize themselves with the several Acts and Orders. (This summary of deer legislation does not include that relating to the harvesting of antler 'velvet'.)

Useful Data

When making records, reasonably accurate estimates of distances, areas, weights and times are desirable. The following data are given for this purpose:

1 acre	Approximately 70 yd by 70 yd
1/10 acre	22 yd by 22 yd
1 hectare	2·47 acres
1 sq. mile	640 acres
Average pace	2½ ft 120 paces Approx. 100 yd
1 ft	30 cm
Fast walking	1 mile in 16 minutes 4 miles per hour
Extended arms	Approx. 6 ft
Kneecap to ground	” 18 in
Span of thumb and little finger	” 9 in
100 lb	45 kg

The time required to say the words 'one second' is approximately 1 second.

Recording

Many male deer can be identified easily in the field from year to year by some characteristic marking or behaviour. Records of individuals, accompanied perhaps by a sketch, are of great value. A great deal can be learned from subsequent identifications of the same animals.

Counting

Estimate from the number of times one can identify *known* males in a day's count in a given area. If fresh unknowns keep appearing then obviously the full total has not been reached. If the same heads are seen over and over again, presumably you are counting most of the deer in the area. See also p. 13.

THE REINDEER COUNCIL OF THE UNITED KINGDOM

Reindeer were re-introduced to Scotland in 1952 after some 800 years, under the auspices of the Reindeer Council of the United Kingdom. In 1970 the herd consisted of 82 head, including 25 calves. A considerable research programme is in progress. Permission to visit the herd can be obtained from the Managing Director, Mr. M. N. P. Utsi, Reindeer Co. Ltd., Aviemore, Inverness-shire, who planned the project and brought the breeding animals from northern Sweden and southern Norway. Parties usually leave Reindeer House daily at about 11 a.m.

The history of the herd is given in Reindeer Council Reports Nos 3–6 and in *Glenmore: Cairngorms*, Forest Park Guide, 1966 (H.M.S.O. Edinburgh). Information about reindeer breeding in general and in the Scottish setting may be sought from Dr. E. J. Lindgren, M.A., Hon. Secretary, Reindeer Council, Newton Hill, Harston, Cambridge.

Where to Go for Information

Parks and zoological gardens—special features

National Zoological Park, Edinburgh. Deer in natural surroundings.

Lowther Wildlife Park, Penrith. Red, fallow, sika. Open access.

Norfolk Wildlife Park, Great Witchingham. All British deer. Close view.

Petworth Park, Sussex. Very fine fallow deer. Open access.

Phoenix Park, Dublin. Colour variations. Fallow. Open access.

Richmond Park, London. Red and fallow deer. Open access.

Warnham Park, Horsham, Sussex. Some of finest red deer in Britain. Advance permission from owner.

Whipsnade Park, Dunstable, Bedfordshire. Ten species available for study. Close view.

Woburn Park, Bedfordshire. Ten species. Open access.

A list of other deer parks is available from the British Deer Society, 7½p.

Private and public museums

British Museum (Natural History), South Kensington, London. A representative collection of British deer. Free.

Private Museum. Dr. P. Delap, White House, Appleby, Westmorland. Deer of the North-West. Advance permission.

Private Museum. G. Kenneth Whitehead, Old House, Withnell Fold, Chorley, Lancs. Deer of the World. Advance permission.

Zoological Museum, Tring, Hertfordshire. Species of world deer. Unusual variations in roe deer. Free.

Forest parks, forest museums and nature trails

Bourn Vincent Forest Park. Bourn Vincent Estate Office, Killarney, Co. Kerry. Forest trails, Muckross Museum. Sika, red deer. Open access.

Cannock Chase. Forestry Commission, Ladyhill, Rugeley, Staffs. Museum, forest trails.

Dean Forest Park. Forestry Commission, Park End, Lydney, Gloucestershire. Forest walks, high seats.

Grizedale. Forestry Commission, Grizedale, Lancashire. Nature trail. Museum and wildlife centre. High seats.

Kielder Forest Park. Forestry Commission, Bellingham, Northumberland. Nature trails, museum, high seats.

Mortimer Forest. Forestry Commission, Forest Office, Ludlow. Special permit for access. Long-haired fallow. High seats, museum.

New Forest. Forestry Commission, Queen's House, Lyndhurst, Hants. Five species of deer. Forest Museum. Sanctuary and forest walks. Advance permission for Museum and Sanctuary.

Randalstown, N. Ireland. Forest Office, Randalstown. Museum. High Seats. Fallow deer.

Wareham. Forestry Commission, Wareham. Nature trail. High seats. Sika deer.

Introduction to the Distribution of Deer in Britain and Eire

In the following pages an attempt has been made to summarize what is known at the present time about the distribution of the various species of deer to be found living in a naturally wild or feral state in Britain and in Eire. Changes in status will continue to occur.

Apart from the naturally wild red and roe deer, and the

herds of fallow deer in the ancient hunting forests, the majority of deer today owe their existence to escape from deer parks, a common occurrence from Cromwellian times, but particularly frequent during and since the two world wars.

Deer are great travellers, especially if they are persecuted, and they will suddenly be observed in the most unlikely places, sometimes far removed from their places of origin. The fact, therefore, that a species is excluded from any county in the following lists does not necessarily imply that it never occurs there. If it is present in an adjoining county, sooner or later it can be expected to cross the county boundaries, for these are obviously no barrier. Mainline railways, however, sometimes prove to be so. Main roads, rivers and built-up areas may deter for a while but even these are eventually circumvented.

In the following tables presence or absence in an area is indicated as follows:
present + ;
absent − .
Counties are indicated by their old names.

THE DISTRIBUTION OF WILD AND FERAL DEER IN ENGLAND

County	Red	Fall.	Sika	Roe	Munt.	Ch.W.
Bedfordshire	−	+	−	−	+	+
Berkshire	−	+	−	+	+	−
Buckinghamshire	−	+	−	−	+	+
Cambridgeshire	−	+	−	−	+	−
Cheshire	+	−	−	−	−	−
Cornwall	+	+	−	+	−	−
Cumberland	+	−	−	+	−	−
Derbyshire	+	+	−	−	−	−
Devonshire	+	+	−	+	+	−
Dorset	−	+	+	+	+	−
Durham	+	+	−	+	−	−
Essex	+	+	−	+	+	−
Gloucestershire	+	+	−	+	+	−
Hampshire	+	+	+	+	+	−
Herefordshire	−	+	−	+	−	−
Hertfordshire	−	+	−	−	+	−
Huntingdonshire	−	+	−	−	+	+
Kent	−	+	+	−	−	−
Lancashire	+	+	+	+	−	−
Leicestershire	−	+	−	−	+	−
Lincolnshire	+	+	−	−	−	−
Middlesex	−	−	−	−	+	−
Monmouthshire	−	+	−	−	−	−
Norfolk	+	+	−	+	+	+
Northamptonshire	−	+	−	−	+	−
Nottinghamshire	+	+	−	−	+	−
Oxfordshire	−	+	−	+	+	−
Rutland	−	+	−	−	+	−
Shropshire	−	+	−	−	−	+
Somerset	+	+	−	+	−	−
Staffordshire	+	+	−	−	+	−
Suffolk	+	+	−	+	+	−
Surrey	+	−	−	+	+	−
Sussex	−	+	−	+	+	−
Warwickshire	−	+	−	−	+	−

N.B. If any reasonable doubt exists as to the presence of wild and feral deer of any given species on a resident breeding basis, they are assumed to be absent from the county or island concerned.

County	Red	Fall.	Sika	Roe	Munt.	Ch.W.
Westmorland	+	−	−	+	−	−
Wiltshire	+	+	−	+	+	−
Worcestershire	−	+	−	−	−	−
Yorkshire						
N. Riding	+	+	−	+	−	−
E. Riding	−	+	−	−	−	−
W. Riding	+	+	+	+	−	−

ISLANDS AROUND ENGLAND

Island	Red	Fall.	Sika	Roe	Munt.	Ch.W.
Brownsea	−	−	+	−	−	−
Lundy	−	−	+	−	−	−

WALES

County	Red	Fall.	Sika	Roe	Munt.	Ch.W.
Anglesey	−	+	−	−	−	−
Breconshire	−	−	−	−	−	−
Caernarvonshire	−	−	−	−	−	−
Carmarthenshire	−	+	−	−	−	−
Denbighshire	−	+	−	−	−	−
Flintshire	−	+	−	−	−	−
Glamorganshire	−	+	−	−	−	−
Monmouthshire	−	+	−	−	−	−
Montgomeryshire	+	+	−	−	−	−
Pembrokeshire	−	−	−	−	−	−
Radnorshire	−	−	−	−	−	−

SCOTLAND (MAINLAND)

County	Red	Fall.	Sika	Roe	Munt.	Ch.W.
Aberdeen	+	−	−	+	−	−
Angus	+	−	−	+	−	−
Argyll	+	+	+	+	−	−
Ayr	+	−	−	+	−	−
Banff	+	+	−	+	−	−
Berwick	−	−	−	+	−	−
Caithness	+	−	+	+	−	−
Clackmannanshire	−	−	+	+	−	−
Dunbarton	+	+	−	+	−	−
Dumfries	+	+	−	+	−	−
East Lothian	−	−	−	+	−	−
Fife	−	−	+	+	−	−
Inverness	+	+	+	+	−	−
Kincardine	+	−	−	+	−	−
Kinross	−	−	−	+	−	−
Kirkcudbright	+	+	−	+	−	−
Lanark	−	−	−	+	−	−
Midlothian	−	−	−	+	−	−
Moray	+	−	−	+	−	−
Nairn	+	−	−	+	−	−
Peebles	−	−	+	+	−	−
Perth	+	+	−	+	−	−
Renfrew	−	−	−	+	−	−
Ross Cromarty	+	+	+	+	−	−
Roxburgh	−	−	−	+	−	−
Selkirk	−	−	−	+	−	−
Stirling	+	−	−	+	−	−
Sutherland	+	+	+	+	−	−
West Lothian	−	−	−	+	−	−
Wigtown	+	−	−	+	−	−

SCOTTISH ISLANDS

County	Red	Fall.	Sika	Roe	Munt.	Ch.W.
Argyllshire						
Islay	+	+	−	+	−	−
Jura	+	−	−	−	−	−
Luing	−	−	−	+	−	−
Mull	+	+	−	−	−	−
Ulva	+	−	−	−	−	−
Scarba	+	+	−	−	−	−
Seil	−	−	−	+	−	−
Buteshire						
Arran	+	−	−	−	−	−
Bute	−	−	−	+	−	−
Inverness						
N. Harris	+	−	−	−	−	−
Pabbay	+	−	−	−	−	−
Raasay	+	−	−	−	−	−
Rhum	+	−	−	−	−	−
Scalpay	+	−	−	−	−	−
Skye	+	−	−	−	−	−
North Uist	+	−	−	−	−	−
Ross-shire						
Lewis	+	−	−	−	−	−

NORTHERN IRELAND

County	Red	Fall.	Sika	Roe	Munt.	Ch.W.
Co. Antrim	−	+	−	−	−	−
Co. Armagh	−	−	−	−	−	−
Co. Down	−	+	−	−	−	−
Co. Fermanagh	+	+	+	−	−	−
Co. Londonderry	−	−	−	−	−	−
Co. Tyrone	+	+	+	−	−	−

EIRE

County	Red	Fall.	Sika	Roe	Munt.	Ch.W.
Carlow	−	+	−	−	−	−
Cavan	−	+	−	−	−	−
Clare	−	+	−	−	−	−
Cork	−	+	−	−	−	−
Donegal	+	+	−	−	−	−
Dunlin	−	+	+	−	−	−
Galway	−	+	−	−	−	−
Kerry	+	−	+	−	−	−
Kildare	−	+	−	−	−	−
L'Aoighis	−	+	−	−	−	−
Leitrim	−	+	−	−	−	−
Leins	−	+	−	−	−	−
Limerick	−	+	−	−	−	−
Longford	−	+	−	−	−	−
Louth	−	+	−	−	−	−
Mayo	−	+	−	−	−	−
Meath	−	+	−	−	−	−
Monaghan	−	+	−	−	−	−
Offaly	−	+	−	−	−	−
Roscommon	−	+	−	−	−	−
Sligo	−	+	−	−	−	−
Tipperary	−	+	−	−	−	−
Waterford	−	+	−	−	−	−
Westmeath	−	+	−	−	−	−
Wexford	−	−	−	−	−	−
Wicklow	+	+	+	−	−	−

EIRE ISLANDS

County	Red	Fall.	Sika	Roe	Munt.	Ch.W.
Co. Dublin Lambay	−	+	−	−	−	−

The British Deer Society

Before 1963 in England and Wales, and 1959 in Scotland, almost the only protection given to our deer was provided by enlightened landowners and a few others. In many places, deer were killed indiscriminately—often with inadequate weapons, regardless of breeding season. The result was frequently terrible cruelty. Under the Deer (in Scotland) Act, 1959, some protection was given to Scotland's deer, but the situation in England and Wales remained unaltered until the passing of the Deer Act, 1963.

In the years preceding 1963, a number of people with various interests in deer, who were members of the Mammal Society, got together and formed the Deer Group within that society. They felt very strongly that matters ought to be improved but, under the rules of that society, they were unable to take active steps. They therefore decided to form a new society, which could do what they felt necessary, and on 24 February 1963, the British Deer Society was formally inaugurated at Woburn in Bedfordshire, a very suitable venue with its superb herds of many species of deer. Members of this newly formed society had already played a very active part in the framing and passing of the 1963 Act.

Since then, the Society had grown rapidly in numbers and, to simplify organization, branches have been formed, covering the whole of England and Scotland, and parts of Wales and Ireland. These have now been grouped together into national areas, each with its own council. Although Society study days and symposia are organized by a Central Council, it is in the branches that real activity takes place. Field and indoor meets, film shows, public meetings and purely social events are held, bringing the members together and publicizing the work of the Society and, at the same time, recruiting new members. Various projects are undertaken, and assistance is given to deer counts and catch-ups. Exhibitions are staged with a view to bringing to the notice of the public the various aspects of the Society's work.

A vital feature of the Society which makes it different to most other groups of similar interests is that it is not a hunter's organization, although the need for properly conducted control is fully recognized, and that the participation of people with every type of interest in deer is welcomed.

The photographer and artist has often, we feel, quite as much to offer as the hunter or the scientist. In the same way, the observant eyes and enquiring mind of a child can frequently notice things which have been overlooked by an experienced adult.

The British Deer Society provides a meeting place for all these people, and it has been found that very often valuable information comes from the most unexpected sources.

This mixing of interests and the resulting mutual understanding provide the main strength of the Society. With such a wide spectrum of interests, we can provide experts in many aspects, and we are finding that more and more we are being asked for advice—not only by private persons, but also by government departments.

Members receive three copies of *Deer* annually—an excellent magazine, designed to suit all tastes. Scientific articles can follow an account of an interesting hunt (stalk), while branch news and venison recipes may appear on neighbouring pages; superb photographs, most of them taken by members, are a special feature. The magazine, it is felt, binds the Society together and is becoming well known in international circles.

We have a number of overseas members in numerous countries, including Scandinavia, the Netherlands, Germany, France and other European countries, India, the United States, South America, Australia and New Zealand. As close a liaison as possible is kept with these people through *Deer*.

The aims of the British Deer Society are:

1 the study and the dissemination of the knowledge of deer;

2 the promotion of proper and humane methods of management, conservation and control of deer;

3 the provision of advice on all matters which relate to deer.

The Headquarters is currently located at The Mill House, Bishopstrow, Warminster, Wiltshire (telephone: Warminster (0985) 216608).

Books Recommended

Cameron A.G. (1923) *The Wild Red Deer of Scotland*. Blackwood.

Carne P.H. (1970) *Wild Deer of the West Sussex Downs*. West Sussex Deer Control Society.

Chaplin R.E. (1977) *Deer*. Blandford.

Chapman D. & N. *Fallow Deer*. T. Dalton, Suffolk.

Corbet G.B. & Southern H.N. (1979) *The Handbook of British Mammals*, 2nd edn. Blackwell Scientific Publications.

Darling F. Fraser (1956) *A Herd of Red Deer*. Oxford University Press.

British Deer Society, Deer in Britain Series (revised): 1, Fallow Deer, D. & N. Chapman; 2, (double volume) Muntjac, O. Dansie and Chinese Water Deer, Arnold Cooke; 3, Sika, M.T. Horwood & E.H. Masters; 4, Roe Deer, P. Delap; 5, Red Deer, P. Delap. British Deer Society.

Fooks H.A. & Prior R. (1978) *Hints on Woodland Stalking*. British Deer Society.

Fooks H.A. & Hotchkis J. (1978) *Deer Control*. British Deer Society.

Harris R.A. & Duff K.R. (1970) *Wild Deer in Britain*. David & Charles.

Hart-Davis, Duff (1978) *Monarchs of the Glen*. Cape.

Holmes F. (1973) *Following the Roe*. Bartholomew & Son.

Krebs H. (1965) *Young or Old?* F.C. Meyer Verlag, Munich.

Lawrence M.J. & Brown R.W. (1968) *Mammals of Britain*. Blandford.

Luxmoore, Edmund (1980) *Deer Stalking*. David & Charles.

MacNally L. (1968) *Highland Year*. Dent.

MacNally L. (1970) *Highland Deer Forest*. Dent.

Millais J.G. (1897) *British Deer and their Horns*. Sotheran.

de Nahlik A. (1959) *Wild Deer*. Faber & Faber.

de Nahlik A. (1974) *Deer Management*. David & Charles.

Prior R. (1976) *Living with Deer*. White Lion Publishers.

Prior R. *Roe Deer: Management and Stalking*. Game Conservancy, Fordingbridge.

Prior R. (1968) *The Roe Deer of Cranborne Chase*. Oxford University Press.

Whitehead G.K. (1950) *Deer and their Management in the Deer Parks of Great Britain and Ireland*. Country Life.

Whitehead G.K. (1960) *The Deer Stalking Grounds of Great Britain and Ireland*. Hollis & Carter.

Whitehead G.K. (1981) *Hunting and Stalking Deer in Britain through the Ages*. Batsford.

Index

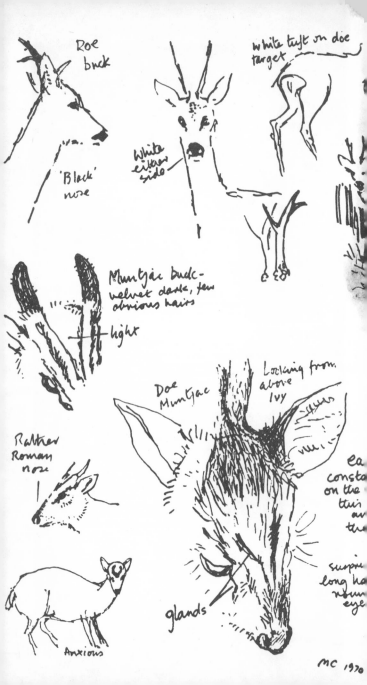

Roe buck

white tuft on doe target

'Black' nose

White either side

Muntjac buck— velvet dark, few obvious hairs

light

Doe Muntjac

Looking from above Ivy

Rather Roman nose

glands

ea consta on the this ar the

suspi long ha noun eye

Anxious

MC 1970